CW00553600

MAPS & ROOMS

Writing from Wales

LUCENT DREAMING

First Edition

Maps and Rooms: Writing from Wales
Published by Lucent Dreaming Ltd.
Rabble Studio, 103 Bute Street, Cardiff, CF10 5AD

Cover design by Joachim Buur and Jannat Ahmed.
Edited by Jannat Ahmed, Samiha Meah and Jonas David.
Illustrated by Jannat Ahmed and Shan Ahmed.

ISBN 9-781-7396609-0-1

The publisher acknowledges the financial support of
Literature Wales, Books Council of Wales and Creative Wales.

All the anthology's contributors were a part of Literature Wales' 2021–22 Representing Wales programme which is supported by the National Lottery through the Arts Council of Wales.

Literature Wales is the national company for the development of literature whose vision is a Wales where literature empowers, improves and brightens lives.

Contents

Contents

Maps and Rooms

Maps and Rooms

Introduction

Umulkhayr Mohamed &
Taz Rahman

Maps are, in their simplest sense, the evidence of an exercise in tracing space driven by discovery. More than this, they have always revealed a human desire to share what we find along the way, to pass on the lessons that our being in the world provides us, with a generosity that is implicit.

Rooms have forever been held spaces, though what they have held is not necessarily a feeling of safety. They can just as easily feel stripped of air and warmth. In contrast to maps that represent the sprawling out of space that is full of detail, the nature of rooms is one of defined limits and edges that can only hold so much. And yet they function as containers of precious things, of lives lived, the everyday, and the potential of consistent comfort, so long as the circumstances allow.

The featured texts provide literary reflections on Maps and Rooms by writers of colour from across Wales, and reveal a long held and layered relationship with place that we hope you cannot help but sit with, and wonder why writers of colour have for so long been asked to centre their writing around their racialised identities.

Maybe it is possible to follow Elizabeth Bishop's advice to 'not get too involved with people who can't possibly understand' and simply get on with the business of creation. Class consciousness and the need to address the balance of who among us gets to tell stories—and for that matter which stories are told, and how inclusive we need to be in our writing—has thankfully progressed.

English fiction has moved on from Salman Rushdie's emergence over a generation and half ago. Post-colonial theory as an academic discipline is now over half a century old. Yet as emerging writers representing the global majority in cultures where we are the immediate minority, our literary creations can still be burdened with the imposition that we need to be more compliant or more diffident. In some circles, there is the expectation that we should either be painting exotic worlds of marigolds, verandas or act as dissident rebels moaning about a different, harsher set of realities in a society where we are still at the receiving end of everyday latent prejudice and the resultant economic and social depravity. The essayists among us are still fighting for the rest of our rights to be at the table, branded as battleaxes or serial moaners for raising their voices.

There is abundant talent in writing about our spaces,

and readers are obviously buying our books now that we are starting to see ourselves emerge from the usual shelves reserved for the previous generation of emerging writers of colour. The #BlackLivesMatter movement has evidently made a little more space for all of us at the margins, in redressing more of the historical imbalance in publishing. However, in publication terms, we are still somewhat restricted to our expected intersections. In readership terms, there is still a long way to go.

The present backdrop of linking ourselves to the spaces we hark from, or our ancestors belonged to, is a necessary tool for all writers. However, there is still too much of 'where I'm from' and too little of 'where we're heading,' and for emerging writers, the latter is the promised land.

We as writers from unrepresented backgrounds should be allowed to enter, run our fingers along the white wisteria floribunda, caress the milkthistle without having to feel the need to colour in this scene with ayurvedic ginger. We should be allowed to soar our own lone enraptured voices in nature, write spooky suspense thrillers, conjure up imagined worlds in space time continuum or at the edge of a forest with climate concerns, without being burdened by questions of colouring in a scene to explain the intersections of where we are coming from, unless we ourselves feel the need to explain this to the reader. The bigger picture of a fossil fuel-dependent planet plunging even deeper into climate crisis and the repercussions resonating in economic and societal chaos are far too important to be still caught up in old expectations.

Here in Wales, there seems to be a long overdue

attempt to redress the balance of who gets to experience the opportunity of development. This is a long-term programme, and one bursary or two cannot redress the imbalance of who writes, who is being published and even more importantly, who gets to develop a taste for reading literature. Creating writers and readers has to be a sustained campaign over a generation. A diverse readership comprises readers from marginalised backgrounds, economically deprived households who bear the brunt of being priced out of literature because of cuts to library funding, and prohibitively expensive and remote literary festivals. All this could not be reversed in a year or two. The present anthology represents a glimpse of contemporary Welsh writing talent in poetry, fiction and autobiographical sketches.

Nia Morais is fast making a reputation as a multi-genre writer. Placing her protagonist in an unfamiliar and long since occupied environment creates an air of suspense that surrounds you as you sit and read this short story, and yet there also remains an undercurrent of comfort coming from Nia's writing as you trust that wherever this story takes you, you'll make it back home in one piece, and richer for it. Her spooky short stories are colourful and atmospheric. Her featured story here is a gothic horror tale of a girl who stumbles across an abandoned limeworks and realises that she might not be alone.

Durre Shahwar has become an important voice in the Welsh literary scene: in all her practices, whether as an artist, editor, writer or speaker, she is at the forefront of pushing boundaries and widening the gate of opportunity for the marginalised. Her piece is a first-person recollection of a series of meetings that made up a short lived but intense relationship with the added burden of distance and taboo.

Marvin Thompson's poetry is sublimely padded in religious references serving as stunningly haunting reminders of what the black body has been subjected to through three centuries of colonisation. The three poems in this selection chart journeys in a slaver's collar and tales of institutionalised and casual racism in the streets of London, Edinburgh and Cardiff spanning multiple eras. This mapping of racial mistreatment through poetic form allows for the repetitious loop of connected destinies to be revealed, clear as road maps. But even more so, what lingers is the truth of those who are kept down: their spirits continue to rise, as here Marvin leaves room for triumph, for self-determination alongside the heavy hurt of these histories.

Emily Burnett is a multi-platform creative with major presence in small screen and theatre as an actor. Her writing often explores identity and unrepresented voices. Her piece explores themes of class and friendship. Starting as a love story, it quickly evolves into a question about opportunities. Emily's piece allows us to explore what is often left unsaid, how we can share care and yet struggle to bridge gaps of structural inequality.

Jaffrin's spoken word and poetry are deeply moving personal accounts of her own journeys as a woman of colour. The two poems combined are pictures of first and second generation immigrant life, the expectations against an eerie reality; brutality at multiple levels is abstracted through stunningly sensual imagery. These poems present a rumination on the weight that expectation can carry with them, enough to shake sturdy foundations of houses that were built to withstand the elements, while not accounting for the weathering that families bring with them, as they make their lives within their walls.

Shara Atashi is a widely published essayist, critic and translator. Her featured story is a homage to the Russian greats Chekov and Dostoevsky through a modern retelling of the Cinderella story, an empowered female who is less interested in silver slippers or the prince who promises a lavish courtly life.

Daniel Howell transcends the confines of conventional existence to show us what remains beyond the visual. His story carries that hint of macabre and is based on an encounter with the other-worldly, a woman who no longer has a physical presence, yet appears unexpectedly to tell another story.

Taz Rahman's poem is a fantasy love story between a wandering soul represented in the form of a shape-shifting heron, and the city of Cardiff. Stories witnessed and overheard around the physical vicinity of Cardiff Castle are weaved into a tapestry of stanzas, a personal ode to the city he loves.

Phil Okwedy's main practice is as old as it comes - the art of storytelling. If maps are the memories of space that we place outside of ourselves, and in doing so seek to ascribe an objectivity to them, perhaps what's stopping us from recategorising them as stories is recognising the imperfection inherent in us all, as a well of creativity to be draw on. Phil is no less engaging when penning autobiographical fiction into paper. The creative non-fiction piece included here is an intriguing invitation to consider whether the way memory functions, it makes unreliable narrators of us all.

Umulkhayr Mohamed is an artist and writer. Her piece is a fascinating exploration of boundaries, definitions and margins, the interplay of the three to signify mapping of zones, the exact points of intersections. The tone, questions posed and that sense of exploring the liminal lends a poetic quality to this exposition.

On behalf of all the writers represented here we would like to pay sincere tribute to Jannat Ahmed, co-editor of this anthology and the publisher of Lucent Dreaming. Without her there would be no anthology and without the bold vision she has for Lucent Dreaming as a publishing house to widen participation by writers from previously unrepresented corners of Welsh society, important voices may remain unheard.

Umulkhayr Mohamed and Taz Rahman

Flames in the Rain

NIA MORAIS

Aberthaw Lime Works stood in a little valley further down the path ahead, its tall chimney reaching up into the dark clouds. The wind flattened the ivy that grew up its brick walls and whistled through the empty, gaping windows.

Millie stopped to watch a flock of seagulls wheeling high above it. Her mother had taken her and Gwilym this way once before, explaining how it had been built in the Victorian era, and had operated for nearly 40 years before a kiln explosion had halted operations briefly, and then for good. As Millie made her way towards it, something tugged at her sleeve. She dragged the wool coat away from the yellow gorse and wobbled, stepping heavily into another puddle, skidding slightly.

A whistle sounded somewhere ahead, and Gwilym snapped to attention. He careened away down the path, taking a left out of sight, and a moment later Millie heard his energetic puppy barks echoing from inside the ruin. She hurried down the path, preparing herself for some boring chat with another dog owner.

A curtain of ivy separated the building from the path; Millie could see where the parasite had taken over the bushes to her left and grown across the branches, before snaking their way up the stone bricks. She ducked underneath and hopped down the uneven stone steps, following the sound of Gwilym's barks to the main ruin.

The room was huge, and completely open to the elements. It wasn't very wide, but it was tall. Millie's eyes skipped over the old stone, tracing the cut-off wooden support beams to the clouds that threatened rain high overhead. It made her feel like she was in a long tunnel, or at the bottom of a well. Gwilym was barking at a wall opposite, near a piece of graffiti that read ANARCHY IS LOVE.

"What you yelling at, Peanut?"

Gwilym turned and bounded toward her, his whole body quivering with excitement. High above, a magpie came to rest on an empty window frame. Millie laughed as Gwilym's wagging tail steered him in wobbly zig zags across the stones.

"Come on, silly billy."

They went through a narrow doorway and into a short passageway that ended in a four-foot drop. To Millie's right, an opening in the wall led up a short slope to a tiny gap in the bricks. Peeking through, she could see a huge cylindrical space that led up to the sky. It must have been the kiln, where workers layered wood and coal over lime pebbles and left it burning for days. To her left, another narrow passageway curved around out of sight. Gwilym leapt into the larger corridor below, following his nose to some end Millie couldn't see. She turned left and followed the smaller passage around.

It was a small path – enough to move through but narrow so that she had to angle her shoulders slightly as she passed. She passed more little openings in the brick wall which threw shafts of grey light onto the puddles at her feet. This side of the building opened onto a view of the saltwater lake, with the sea wall on the far side and the steel-grey waves pounding the rocky beach beyond that. Millie stood at the entrance, watching the wind drag and shake the gorse bushes all around her. The wind whistled behind her and pushed at her back; there was another drop here, so she moved backwards and crossed her arms against the cold. The rain had begun to fall again, and she already dreaded walking back home without – what her mother would call – a 'proper' coat. If she stayed here until the rain stopped, would her parents notice? If she stayed all day, all night, would they care?

She felt very small in this tall building.

" –Telling you, I saw someone," came a voice from somewhere outside.

She stiffened, tilting her head to catch the voice, but it had been whipped away by the wind. She looked around for

Gwilym, but he was out of sight in the bushes somewhere.

"Came this way?" mumbled another, deeper voice.

"Yeah, man. I saw her."

Millie's stomach turned to cold quicksilver as she heard them again. It could have been anything, a totally innocent remark – it could even have been the dog walker she imagined earlier – but her instincts knew better. How silly to assume she was alone in the ruin, when she had so easily accessed it herself. The two masculine voices were hard to place, coming nearer then drifting further away as the wind played through the empty tunnels of the building. She backed away from the entrance of the passage and retreated a couple feet back the way she had come.

"Have some fun?"

"Yeah, yeah." They were close together. She heard laughing, the crisp hiss of a can cracking open. She stood frozen, staring into the darkness of a tunnel opposite her, six feet above the wide corridor that Gwilym had disappeared through. Were they behind her? Could she jump the gap into the dark tunnel? Should she ring someone? Scream? Attack? Hide?

Millie heard laughing, then shushing as a rock hit the walls of the main room. They were behind her, through the curving tunnel, but how far behind she couldn't tell. She was staring into the dark across the gap too wide to jump. Her knees trembled. The sickening realisation hit her –

The darkness in front had eyes.

Maps and Rooms

Rooms

DURRE SHAHWAR

I believe in God, I say, and he says, *Do you?* But he isn't really all that surprised. I nod. *How many do you believe in?* he asks. *Just one.* Outside, it has started raining and I think of how everyone coming in will see us. We are sitting on the front table and all the tables around us are empty. Everyone else has taken the side ones. The ones that your gaze doesn't directly fall on when you walk into the restaurant, stand in the queue, and contemplate what size fries you're having and would you like a drink with that? Inside, it feels like the neon lights lay us bare to the shadows outside the window, sulking in the October rain. I contemplate the off chance of us bumping into someone we know eating chicken and fries at eight thirty pm at the Queen Street KFC and so I scan every customer. A thirty-something woman with a pram waits for her husband. A twenty-something couple sits close together in another booth. They're closer than we are. I wonder how we look to them, sitting opposite each other. I wonder whether they can tell if he is much older than I am, or whether the colours of our skin contrast in the right way. Whether we look not quite like strangers still navigating the early awkwardness of first meetings.

What about all those other religions? he asks. It's just one God, different names, I say. I don't believe in God, he says. Somehow, I know this already, so I nod. Then he grins and says, *What about Zeus?* And I can't imagine not staring at the deep wrinkle on the corner of his left eye again. Later, when we walk out with our fingers loose in each other's and our footsteps falling in and out of rhythm, he says, *I believe in Zeus.*

352. That was the first one with paper-thin walls and a view over the derelict building on the construction site. At one point, he stood at the window, gestured, and said *Nice view*, but it didn't matter. We never really opened the blinds. We never really looked at much except the tones of our skin side by side. Afterwards he asks me what God would think of this and I say, *I don't know.*

When I see him next, the trees are dry, naked of the yellow leaves that were blooming the last time. At night, the shadowed buildings of the city glow from the rain and Christmas lights. We walk past the Christmas market with its smell of hot buns, melted chocolate, and mulled wine and cider. Past the High Street shops, past the castle with a wide strip of blue lights running around it like a ribbon. I imagine unlocking the gates and walking through the castle grounds and into the unknown on the other side. I can't help but point out how pretty it all looks. When he smiles and turns to look at me, I see the lights reflected in his black eyes.

513. *This is the poshest one we've been in yet,* he says, while telling me about the birthday I couldn't celebrate with him. Outside, leaves are growing in place of the ones that fell away in the winter. When I tell him about the mosque, he asks me what I pray for. I scan his face for signs of provocation but find none. I tell him I pray for clarity as he rubs the soles of my feet. In the morning, we linger outside the train station, waiting until the very last second the train pulls up to the platform to leave.

Each time was the last time, yet a few weeks later, we would get away again from our separate lives and spend two days in one city, one room. There were good rooms and bad rooms. Rooms with no paintings or kettles, rooms with bunk beds, rooms that felt clinical like hospital rooms and rooms with showers too small to turn in. Each time, the restaurants were different too and I would think, it's a good thing there are so many.

Each time I went back home and lay in bed. My mother asked me if I was sick, and I said no. She asked if I was depressed, and I said no. Should she call a doctor? No. I couldn't explain to her how I could feel the blood underneath my pores every second now. In the night, my feet would find the empty spaces in the covers that neither warmth, nor I could occupy. When reading, I'd spend hours on a chapter, straightening out words from left to right repeatedly as though ironing out a stubborn crease. Behind my eyes there was always another story, another chapter being read and reread. If I remembered every tiny detail, every step in the right order, I could hold on to it. But memory was blurry like my short-sighted eyes.

Those days, being was easy. We would forget about everything but the ticking of the clock. It was as though a layer of me existed outside of me, apart from myself. Our eyes would look on unashamed, unapologetic at every blemish, every hair. And then we would collect our limbs, untangle where my hand ended and his arm started, figure out which foot was his and which was mine. And we would drag our tired bodies out and leave our shapes in the white sheets. We never tidied after us. I never really thought about who was there before us or who would be there after. They just became our rooms. And that's how I remember them. With the bathroom light falling on closed blinds, crumpled sheets, and the heavy scent of what we leave behind lying thick in the air. With one foot in and one foot out, I would turn and look back at each room, checking for forgotten items, just before the door closed.

Maps and Rooms

Poems

BY MARVIN THOMPSON

Composed Upon Westminster Bridge, October 12, 1774

Lords sip sweet teas and spit: *Go home negro.*
Is home Grenada's cane fields or Greenwich
or Mayfair, selling sugar? Slave name's Sancho,

Ignatius for pomp. Each dusk, my heart follows
the call of gin to quell my ache, its pitch.
As street smoke swirls, dames shout: *Go home negro,*

their grins dark as molasses. Mizzle slows.
I write minuets; they sneer at my fat lips,
my ape nose. Guinea's rot is in my soul.

When Gainsborough asked me to smile, I said no,
not drunk enough. This city's spires sit
like angels whispering: *Go home negro.*

This noon, my wife bellowed: 'Blood built these domes:
dump your stock in the Thames. We'll be broke
but we'll have better lives.' She laughed: 'We're the Sanchos,

the first Blacks under these oaks and shadows
to choose who chokes us for taxes.' A boat
ploughs the brown river. Gin's a stone's throw
from my face; the dusk air sweetens. I stroll home.

How to Remove a Slaver's Collar from your Neck (in Three Easy Steps)

1. In the dirt of an Edinburgh alleyway, float into dreams of your mother, a plantation midwife

Grasping a lantern in the sweat of August, a bearded man breaks
your reverie, his breath hot on your face: 'Are you Esther?'
You're in half-dream, crow wings sprouting from your mother's back.

He pays the farthing before you run into his house, bed soaked
with his wife's womb blood. The room shudders.
From unpaid mansion scrubber, mud washer, to red and wailing life:

you hand holy joy to the panting wife,
mother, daughter of God. In the cresting night, she holds her first daughter
to breathe at birth, eyes bright as your mother's back.

**2. On your way to the town jail, when your captor's cart
hits a rock, work your magic**

Hogtied in road mud, you eye the waxing gibbous moon,
    stretch your neck.
A horse's wet nose rests on your leg, cold and still as your
    collar.
The husband spits: 'The advert said two guineas for the
    black

but how much for a witch? How loud will the town cheer
when you burn?' Your mouth quakes: 'Should I make
    your daughter's heart stop?'
You return to reverie, two wings spreading across your
    mother's back.

3. Relish the release

You watch the collar fall and clang at your feet: a flock of
    crows flecks
the horizon. The husband pays the blacksmith and you
    saunter
through the market's breath, its chicken and pig stink.
You return to the memory: washing blood from your
    mother's back.

An excerpt from Top Ten Tips for Surviving a Lynching

Tip 1

Fill your mind with lines from Psalm 19,
the cadences you learnt, Emmett, in pews
and replayed, sipping cola in June's sheen.
The man gouging your eye out isn't news
to God who saw, in tableau, what would be
before creation: Black calves, dangling toes;
Mississippi's August air, the bees,
thousands of Black throats, church hats below;

flies riding the Cardiff prison breeze.
The thick love of Mahmood's smile is the thick
of your smile. The stench of your innocence
is known to Allah and South Wales police
yet a noose is fitted tight around your neck.
You ask Allah, 'Where is the evidence?

Tip 2

You ask The Lord, 'Where is the evidence?'
If you lynch a man you fill a thousand minds
with terror. Learn your place and the ten cents
your 14-year-old eyes are worth. Crows find
Mahmood hanging softly below Welsh clouds.

He's British – Somaliland's a colony.
Let Negros vote? The congregation's loud,
ready to cut off keepsakes. Oak trees

sigh as you kick, kick, kick... where's Allah?
How much are your Somalian eyes worth?
Rain dribbles from rope to clavicle.
Your upper cervical spine weakens, dogs
yap in the distance, loud as noon church.
An angel stands, wings held horizontal.

Tip 3

An angel stands, wings held horizontal,
1955, hazel leaves brown.
To onlookers, she is invisible.
To you, a prayer answered on prison ground?
In red hijab and robe, her singing cuts
through you like Welsh bayonets, like hope.
A song your mother used to sing, the jut
of her wings shadows the yard below the rope:

a song for Allah in Cardiff. The blood
of Christ sung in Mississippi for us
like love, Black families fleeing the South,
the night roads dark as crows and Noah's flood.
Sing, 'Go Down, Moses' amidst dead-skin dust
in a police interview room with your lost mouth.

Maps and Rooms

Raya and Tom

EMILY BURNETT

Raya's breath catches in the back of her throat. The saliva in her mouth speeds up its production and she is intensely aware that she needs to swallow. Her body seems to halt instead, unable to do things independently.

Breathe. Swallow. Blink. Swallow again. Breathe. Breathe.

"Hey Tom..."

Raya hasn't seen Tom in over six months. This isn't that long in the grand scheme of things, but at seventeen all Raya wants is for life to speed up, for something to begin. The last few years felt like a slow crawl towards the opening night of her life. Though lately, after all the anticipation, she fears the reviews might only fetch a mediocre 'two stars', leaving the show of *life* with much room for improvement.

The last six months without Tom may as well have been years. Raya hadn't been sure what to expect from their distance. They'd spent the entirety of their youth together out of circumstance rather than choice. He'd lived up the road from Raya, in a house that she only later acknowledged was substantially larger than her own. They'd attended the same primary school, and the same secondary. They shared the same saxophone teacher at the age of seven, and often found themselves sat next to each other in class due to similar academic abilities. It was inevitable that they would become best friends.

Now that she thinks about it, six months is probably the longest they've ever been apart.

Seeing Tom now, standing at her front door, something feels off. He is wearing a short sleeve polo shirt and shorts that she's never seen before. His thick, dark hair is much longer than when he left. His smile looks the same, except Raya notices it is more conscious of itself now, more thought through. But it is none of these things that make her forget how to, *breathe, blink, swallow.* It is none of these things that she'll remember later in bed, lying awake with the sheets clinging to her body. No. What she will remember are his shoulders. His shoulders are huge. How, in six months, had his shoulders gone from skinny boy shoulders, to this? She hasn't even finished reading *A Suitable Boy* yet.

"Hey you…"

Tom leans in to give Raya a hug. They've been hugging forever, the sensation is commonplace, but now these big shoulders lead to big arms, and a broad back, that simply envelopes her. Raya breathes him in. He smells like fresh laundry and that grassy, airy smell of fresh sweat made outdoors. She knows it's weird, but she finds comfort in the fact that, if he squeezes hard enough, he could crush her.

"You ready to go?" he says with an 'end of hug' squeeze.

"Yea, I'll just grab my keys."

"Is your mum in? I thought I would say hi."

"No. Sorry. You'll have to flirt with my mum some other time."

Tom laughs. "You're disgusting."

"You have no idea." She doesn't say it for a reaction, but she purposefully holds his gaze.

***

When Tom got his letter to confirm his scholarship for Hutching's College, he wasn't sure how to break the news to Raya. He'd practiced in the mirror and everything. He watched his own face deliver the news, experimenting to find equal amounts of happiness and regret. They discussed every decision they made ever since decisions felt important, but the choice to apply for Hutching's in the first place was something he hadn't shared. He didn't think he would get in, and if he did, he didn't think he would get the scholarship he needed to supplement the £40,000 a year boarding and tuition fee. His parents had money, but not that kind of money. He kept the letter hidden for three weeks before he finally told her. On that day, Raya had smiled, and hugged him, happy enough, but all the way home they couldn't find the room to talk about anything else.

"So, have you made some good friends then?" Tom watches Raya twiddle with the frayed edge of her denim shorts as she speaks. They walk past The Old Rectory and onto the bridal path that leads up to the woods. He walks alongside her with his hands in his pockets, the millimetre of warm air between them stroking his arm.

"Yea. Yea. I've got a good mate in my boarding house. He's also called Tommy, it's kind of annoying."

"Wow. Tom and Tommy. You're cool."

Tom gently pushes her off the path. "You have no idea."

Raya looks up at him. Her big, brown eyes wide. Tom knows he's testing her, but he doesn't know why. For a moment he thinks he might have won a round of their game, but as quick as the thought lands, the ball flies back into his court.

"Is he fit?"

"I thought you were seeing that guy...?"

"That guy...? You went to school with him for 4 years Tom. I'm sure you can find a name."

"Frank...? Fr...?" Tom knows he's being a dick, but *Freddy Jones* always had that effect on him.

"It's Freddy. And you know it's Freddy."

"Freddy – Yea him. What happened to him?"

Raya hesitates. Tom waits for a response. The millimetre of warm air on his bare arm gets hotter.

"We broke up three months ago."

The corners of Tom's lips turn upwards, a smile only he will ever know existed. Match point.

They walk on in silence. It's not uncomfortable. It's a silence they've happily occupied over the years. The last time they saw each other, Tom was leaving to go to Hutching's. He'd said he'd be back for Christmas and Easter, but then offers to attend holiday homes in the Caribbean and skiing chalets in the Alps got in the way. Time hadn't moved slowly for Tom. Knocking on Raya's door earlier, it felt like he only left her yesterday. But now, walking up the path towards the woods, he realises more time has passed than he'd thought. He watches Raya, the way she fidgets as she walks, the frizzy bits of her hair sticking to her temples, wet with sweat and he avoids the urge to edge into his one-millimetre *safe* distance from her.

"I'm sorry I wasn't back at Easter. I wanted to come home, I just --"

"Couldn't turn down the 1st class flight to Switzerland?"

"That's not fair."

Raya laughs. "Oh, you're right. Your luxury holidays really aren't fair."

"What's your problem, Raya?"

"Me. Oh no, I'm fine, Tom, don't worry about me."

Tom stops walking. He places his hand on Raya's shoulder and pulls her back to face him.

"Let go of me, Tom."

"What is wrong with you?"

He places a hand on her bare arm. Raya looks at it and then up at him. It's a look Tom doesn't recognise, it's sad and confusing and turns the warm air between them cold. It scares Tom because he knows their game is over.

***

"Raya, what's wrong? Just tell me."

Raya can't answer. She looks at him, at his new hair, his new clothes, his big shoulders, and she can't answer. She doesn't know how to. She just looks at him.

He pulls his hand away from her arm. She misses it the minute it's gone.

"You would have gone too if it was you. You would have left me too."

10 months and 8 days ago was the day Tom's letter arrived. It didn't occur to Raya to google Hutching's College before. When Tom told her he'd got a place there for his A-Levels, she was too pre-occupied with his leaving to consider where he was going. It was only the night before she was

due to see him, lying in bed, illuminated by the artificial glow of her phone screen, that she typed it into Google. She didn't know anything about Hutching's College, or what it was like. She had actively not thought about it, but what she found was beyond anything she could have imagined. Whether it was the 400 acres of beautifully kept land, or the breath-taking architecture of the buildings, or the list of extra-curricular activities that took up two separate pages – Raya never knew education could look like that. Her sixth form barely had flushing toilets, the books in the library had missing pages, and in the music studio, you had to fight for the keyboard that still played F sharp. Education for Raya was surviving, it was defying odds and pushing to be exceptional, but in this place, exceptional was the default. It was a given – with a swimming pool and a squash court thrown in for free.

Now, standing in front of Tom with his big shoulders, after six months apart, for the first time in her life Raya feels small. Small and angry. Not angry that he got in, or that that he had left her and was growing and thriving. But angry that he'd never told her it existed. This magical place, with a price tag they both knew she couldn't afford. This magical place that she knows she would have loved, too.

This magical place that has made her beautiful Tom, dirty.

Breathe. Swallow. Blink.

Poems

BY JAFFRIN

Abbu

My father gathered the dirt under his feet
and watered it with his sweat.
Built a house and a home
with the callus of his hands,
a ground scorched with love
of a new-born family,
bonds bound in blood
across the tables of warmth.
Heart chambers healthy.
Smells of spice line nostrils,
rings of laughter echo in ears,
family portraits glossed in pride.

Abbu 2.0

When the same hands he'd built our home with
become clenched fists,
trying to grip grits of sands
made from all the shattered glass
of the glossed family portraits,
each grain wears a weight
of loving memories licked with animosity.
Eyes haemorrhaged with red,
jaw clicked with stubbornness,
twisted neck bound in anger
from all the chips collected
from his hollowed shoulders
because of the money that could have been
and the imaginary house with a driveway,
food that didn't make it on the table in time.
All the cracks in the pictures
that were meant to be perfect,
let all the human spill out
and show itself accidentally on purpose.
We were buried in the sand
wearing sore-cheeked smiles,
battling gravity
with an anchor of pride tied to our ankles.

The Pilgrim

SHARA ATASHI

Five minutes before midnight, Olenka arrived at the North Greenwich tube station only to see the last train swoosh away through the tunnel.

By this time her black boots were already rubbing the skin of her swollen feet. As she walked to the bus stop to look for a night bus, Olenka remembered that she had forgotten her old trainers at the ball. She had taken them with her in case she needed to change when her feet got tired. You have to do that in London. They were the shabbiest, but also the most comfortable shoes she owned. It wouldn't be a loss to forget them, or so she had thought. Now that it had happened, she needed them more than ever, but there was no going back to the ball. Not after that goodbye ceremony and all that drunken hurly-burly.

The shiny black boots were merciful all day. They had carried Olenka through the city on that warm September

Sunday. One of her postponed plans to walk through this once loved and now reviled city had taken shape. Setting off before midday from Marble Arch, where only a plaque commemorates the site of the horrific executions at Tyburn, she had walked the course of the subterranean River Tyburn northwards to the summit of Primrose Hill to watch the setting sun. The clear view of London was breath-taking, but the crowd of tourists made it difficult to imagine how the city's famous mad poet had once conversed with his spiritual sun at this very spot nearly two hundred years before. Only an inscription in stone informed those who wanted to know what he had done. From there, Olenka walked down to Greenwich in the south-east, where the ball was to take place in an enormous arena owned by a phone company.

Now at midnight, the boots were kneading the skin of her toes and heels, Olenka could feel the slow formation of little blisters. She recalled the trainers, a pair of worn out running shoes in an Aldi plastic bag; the explosions in the front where the toes are, the fabric softened and torn by wear, and the flattened but cushion-like soles. Olenka imagined the person's face who would find the plastic bag and see the magnificent specimen.

At the bus stop the jabber and laughter of a group of night owls filled the starry night. Observing them passively, Olenka's reflections wandered back to the ball, a masquerade of a feast. Almost all the guests had dressed in black garments, wearing the typical trinketry of good old days: silver chain necklaces and bracelets, skull and cross-bone rings, tattoos, black lipstick with matching fingernails.

For herself, Olenka had only obeyed the blackness of the dress code – a knee-length skirt and a blouse with a wide neckline and the pair of workers' black boots.

Inside the darkened arena, from her place on the highest balcony, Olenka enjoyed a full view of the mass. The venue was vast and unreal as a giant spaceship. Twenty thousand people from all over the world had gathered here for this masquerade, to forget reality and time for a few hours. The twinkling of smartphones in the dark reminded Olenka of fireflies – an enormous swarm of them. Her younger years passed before her eyes like a film, like shadow puppetry. How she had tried to adjust herself to the mass all her life until solitude prevailed.

Olenka still did not know who had sent her the strange invitation; fine old-fashioned handwriting in silver on a black card announcing time and place accentuated by the drawing of a candle burning at both ends.

A bus arrived. It would take Olenka to Holborn from where it wouldn't take long to walk to her hotel. She stepped in and sat down, propping her head against the window and letting her mind drift again. Her sore feet faded into oblivion for the moment. Quite suddenly, the freakish guy from the ball jumped into her mind. He didn't seem to belong to the audience; barefoot, medium height, about forty years of age, and dressed in nothing but a loincloth. His outfit was not the only reason why Olenka had noticed him. Each time she left the arena for a cigarette, she saw him standing in a corner staring at her. He had a very high brow and a slim, pointed hook nose. His brown, uncombed hair hung down in thick tresses over his shoulders. At one point, while passing him, she noticed his strange eyes. They were yellowish green and one of the pupils was larger than the other. His face reminded her of Mona Lisa, relaxed cheeks and a smile that was motionless, as if cast on his face for ever. A typical metropolitan loony, she had thought.

Recalling him now, Olenka wondered whether he had been an apparition, only visible to her. Apparently, none of her friends had noticed him, but Olenka did not mention him either. Although, she and a few other people all laughed about the woman, a door keeper at the arena who stood there, forced into a formal dark blue suit with large, white angel wings attached to it.

It happened from time to time that Olenka caught sight of someone who gave her this idea of an apparition – sometimes a pale, cadaverous junky, other times an old, emaciated man who would greet and smile at her. This man, too, in his loincloth somehow looked familiar. As if she had seen him before.

II

Olenka had led a quiet and solitary existence for a long time.

Three years earlier, having resigned from civil service and receiving her early pension – an insignificant amount as it turned out – Olenka decided to leave London for good and move to a suburb where it was easier to find decent accommodation. The month was October, the weather damp, windy and cold, and as gloomy as the sadness that was tearing at her heart. On her way home she calculated that it was possible to live on the means at her disposal for two or three years – counting intervals with black bread and coffee, even four. After studying all the advertisements which were fixed at shop windows of property agents, and still undecided, she jumped on the next train to Southend-on-Sea, took the first dark attic that was offered to her and moved in within a week.

Southend-on-Sea, with its beautiful white houses and the enormous pier that stretched deep into the sea, had become a sinister home to pirates and people-smugglers; London's claws had reached that far, less than an hour by train. But elsewhere ratholes were being let at astronomical amounts. There, Olenka shut herself up as if in a cloister, as if abandoning the rest of the world for ever. By the end of the three years, she had become a complete hermit.

Olenka had become a hermit without noticing it. The other life, the one from her younger years, had been noisy, restless, and as bustling as the city she lived in, but eventually faded away as if washed clean from her consciousness. It wasn't entirely forgotten though. From time to time she received a message or a phone call from an old friend, but her familiarity with that old life had ceased in a way that made her unsociable.

Now, as a woman in her middle ages, Olenka returned to an old passion that made her feel like an infant again. This passion was reading – incessantly, ceaselessly, one book after another. She was sailing away from the spheres of practical day-to-day activities. Devoured by her longing, she had deprived herself of fresh air and nourishing food. With time her skin turned pale grey, her eyes now deeply set in a thin face.

The creatures from the books developed daemonic vitality. They did not retreat from her. Not even when she laid a book down to have her tea with black bread. They did not age. They refused to withdraw as annoying guests sometimes do. Instead, they became permanent subjects like roommates, sometimes calm and understanding, sometimes like close relatives who drew her into disquieting conversations. They even knocked at her door. They sat at her bedside. In her sleep she dreamed of river Thames telling her the names of her drowned friends and explaining to her in detail how she would find them.

There wasn't any order, any preordained system in her life during this time. And new books piled on other books. The bookshelves would soon collapse under their weight. Such was Olenka's state of mind when the strange invitation to the ball slipped through her letterbox.

At first, Olenka put it on the pile of other mail to be ignored. Yet after an hour or so, out of an unknown instinct, she took it from the pile to have a closer look. No sender, no name. Just: *Come on the last day of this September to the Arena at North Greenwich to celebrate with old friends the fortieth anniversary of an old idol's debut. Hour: seven o'clock in the evening. See you there!*

As if for the first time, Olenka began thinking about something that wasn't from any of her books. One or two of her friends came to her mind who could have sent the invitation. Yet the enclosed ticket! Who had made her such a gift, she could not imagine. She could recall a famous singer from old days, a true Orpheus with eyes as black as coal and a voice that could brave storms and wild animals.

Her recollections drifted to her younger years as she opened the wardrobe to see if there was anything suitable for such a ball.

There were a few black suits from her office days, some black skirts and coats. And there were the shiny black boots in workers' style. The hint at an *old idol* made it predictable to her what the style of the event would be, and, if she decided to go at all, she wanted to remain inconspicuous. She tried a few outfits, and, little by little a desire to break out of her home took shape in her. It even awakened a faint blush on her deathlike pallor.

She remembered the circumstances that led to her early retirement from civil service three years earlier. In the months preceding her retirement she became more and more overwhelmed by an odd ecstasy and would throw herself into the streets to look at people. Often she entered into casual conversation with them. Her reason was so obscured that she sometimes didn't know whether the people she saw were real or not. A street sweeper on her street, dark-coloured with long dreadlocks, appeared to be the reincarnation of Hafez, the Persian poet. He always pierced her with his green metallic eyes and swept only the steps at her front door, not any other house. Then he would sit there and have his lunch.

At work she began to deliver her reports in verse. Her manager, a kind man with a generous heart, found it amusing at first, especially because Olenka was one of his most hardworking people. But as the reports written in verse became more frequent and the department faced a backlog in the actual workload, he had to have a word with her. It was after that talk that she became gloomy. She realised that people were giving her strange, coarse looks. She saw that they took her for a mad woman, which wasn't far off the mark.

These revived memories cast a shadow on Olenka now. For the first time since her seclusion she began to spend time in reflections on real life again. Inside her an idea was growing, something with a life of its own that wanted to get out into the world. Even an idea of a future began to take shape in her imagination.

The ball was only a few days ahead.

III

The bus stopped somewhere near central London, not yet at Holborn. As it remained idling there, muttering rose amongst the passengers and the bus driver growled something back at them, but Olenka was absent-minded. It was only after all the other passengers had left the bus that the bus driver shouted in her direction. *Hey lady, you need to get out. This bus ain't go any further.*

Olenka stepped out of the bus and walked up the street. The junctions were blocked to cars. Not even a black cab was within sight. Some drunken object staggered against another staggering object and they both fell against the shutters of a shop. Workers on high cranes were installing Christmas decorations from one side of the street to the other. A black woman was loudly swearing to the sky. *Hey Jesus Christ! See what they're doing in your holy name in September? Why you let them suspend the night bus for your birthday party? Can you tell me how to get home now?*

Olenka came to the corner of Tottenham Court Road and Oxford Street without realising how. The blisters on her feet came to life again. Her hotel in Covent Garden wasn't far, but she wasn't sure how she'd make it there with her sores. A woman who had lost her way asked her how to get to Bayswater. Olenka walked with her to the next bus station where a few people were waiting. There weren't any busses there either. They both walked from one corner to another, from one bus station to another, but all busses had been suspended for the Christmas decorations. They arrived somewhere near Euston. Olenka told the woman there would be a better chance to get a night bus and said goodbye. Her feet kept swelling. Now she had to walk all the way back.

She passed through many streets and squares like an alien outcast. Now that she had left the safety of her dark attic and returned to London, the old city was telling her that she was one from the mass, although it had never been easy to mark off some sort of space for herself among them.

The city wasn't noisy and bustling at this hour. It was past two in the morning. The deserted streets of Soho took Olenka to Piccadilly Circus. Apart from one or two, all pubs were closed. Myriads of black bin bags adorned the Brewer Street and Olenka wondered, as she used to in the past, who might be living under the red lights behind those closed curtains, and whether they were able to pay their rents. As the reality was weighing her down, she sensed in herself the good old instinct of a witness. A new book was unfolding before her and she was permitted to read between the lines.

Under the light of a lamppost, Olenka noticed that her own shadow resembled Quasimodo. She shrank away in disgust. Her mouth was dry; she almost collapsed with each step. She could feel her blisters oozing. Then it appeared, the neon sign of her hotel above the row of buildings, just as she thought she couldn't go any further.

Upon reaching the steps, Olenka caught sight of the loony in the loincloth. He was standing there with his Mona Lisa grin, looking in her direction. In his hand he held the Aldi plastic bag.

"Who the hell are you?" Olenka asked. "What do you want from me?"

"Be seated, my dear child, and don't shout. There is nothing to be afraid of. I just wanted to bring you your shoes."

Olenka couldn't stay standing another second. She sat down on the steps and covered her face with both hands. The stranger sat down beside her, and they were silent for about ten minutes. There was no sound at all, not even that of a faraway engine.

Then, Olenka drew in the fresh air in deep eager breaths, and tried to get up, still contemplating how to get rid of the loony. As if paralysed, she couldn't move a limb. All of a sudden, the thudding of hooves filled the air. They became louder, now accompanied by the neighs of a horse. Olenka realised she was slowly fainting.

"Who's that? I ... know this ... it's my father's horse ...I dreamt of it the other night." Olenka could hear her own voice as if it came through a radio.

"Don't worry my child. It'll pass."

"Am I dying? I'm not ready...not yet ..." the words came out of her in a whisper.

"Nobody dies." The stranger laughed, and his laugh sounded like the neighing of a horse. "Come now, I'll take you to your room. You may fall down the stairs, kid."

Olenka had no strength to get up and walk by herself. Panic rose inside her and numbed her body. The stranger carried her to her room on his shoulder. He placed her on the bed, removed the boots from her feet, and gave her a glass of water. Thin trails of blood and slime from her blisters smudged the white sheet. The looney remained seated on a chair, waiting for Olenka to fall asleep.

Early in the morning, Olenka awoke from a deep sleep. It took her a while to remember the previous day. There wasn't a trace of the stranger. Moving her hands over her face, she realised something sticking to her forehead. She pulled it and looked at it. It was a beautifully hand-painted tarot card of the Hermit.

"What a loony," she murmured and shook her head, looking at the Blue-Tac on the backside of the card.

While drinking hot strong coffee at the hotel lobby, Olenka could hear his last words whispering in her ears. *Nobody dies. You will have all the time you need to prepare your own shroud. But you have to start now.*

Olenka smiled a serene smile. The sun's rays warmed her face. Now she would go back home in her shabby old trainers. She would look for a job in a coffeeshop and wander about the town she had been hiding from for such a long time. She recollected the kind faces of all the shopkeepers in her neighbourhood, the old lady with her bright-coloured dress at the library, the busy platforms of the railway station with crowds of exhausted people commuting to London – and the pirates. She could now embroider them on her shroud.

Maps and Rooms

Dead Woman Running

DANIEL HOWELL

The first time I saw the woman in green, her neck was obviously broken. Even as she jogged past, her head was wrenched down and to the right, and fragments of vertebrae were piercing the left side of her throat. Her skull was slumped onto her shoulder and bounced in time with her stride. I saw her from across the car park. She was wearing a lime green lycra running outfit, and she disappeared behind a grubby red Ford.

I was slow to react, staying rooted to the spot for precious seconds before persuading my legs to carry me over there. Expecting to see a twitching corpse sprawled out on the tarmac, but instead seeing... nothing. No woman, no blood, no lime green yoga pants.

"LEWWWIS!"

I flinched at the shout and spun just in time to get

rugby-tackled by a miniature reflection of myself.

"You're back!" Alfie cheered.

"I'm back," I agreed.

And I forgot about the woman in green, because what else was I supposed to do?

***

The second time I saw the woman in green was from inside Dad's car. It was just like old times: Mum and Dad up front, me and Alfie in the back. Alfie was in his football kit, fiddling with his shin pads. Mum was asking for even more details about how my tour had gone. I was making the same "it was *magical*" pun for the umpteenth time. Alfie was asking me to show him a trick, and I said that I would: provided his team won 8-0.

I saw something green from the corner of my eye and looked out the back window. And there she was: closer this time. She was crossing the road right behind us, her neck still shattered. Bone fragments must have sliced open her jugular, because bloody droplets sprayed upwards with each stride she took.

This time, I saw the woman's face. I had no idea who she was. She made it across the street and disappeared down Hackton Road.

I asked if anybody else had seen that. Nobody had.

***

The third time I saw the woman in green, she was closer still. We were at the dinner table, eating lamb curry and yellow rice.

"*Pleeease*, Lewis?" Alfie was begging. "Just this once! I promise I'll never tell anyone!"

I shook my head. "That's exactly what *I* promised when *I* learned the trick."

And then I looked up, and the woman in green was running right past the window. Her blood splattered against the glass. Her head lolled grotesquely towards me.

I shot out of my seat and ran for the window, but the woman was out of sight within a second. Mum asked me what was wrong. I ignored her, sprinting out into the hallway instead, and bursting through the front door. The woman in green was gone. And from this side of the glass, I could see no blood on the dining room window. No bloody trail along the pavement.

No sign that she'd ever been here.

***

The next day, I drove Alfie to school. He would not stop nagging me. I'd slept badly. I was preoccupied. It was a moment of weakness, and he wore me down.

"Fine!" I snapped. "I'll tell you how I did the trick!"

Alfie grinned, the breeze from the open windows whipping his hair into a triumphant frenzy.

"The other day, when I surprised you at school," I said. "Do you remember the shirt I was wearing?"

He didn't remember.

"It had a picture of a knight on it. The chess piece. And below that, a tick, a letter M, and a number 8. Check-m-eight. Checkmate. Get it?"

He didn't get it.

"That doesn't matter. The point is, I had a number 8 on my shirt. Later you asked to play on my phone. You remember the passcode?"

That one he *did* remember: eight-zero-eight-zero.

"Exactly. The evening I did the trick: how many of us were in the room?"

And suddenly, Alfie understood. That night, Auntie Hannah had been working late, but Uncle Zack had brought the kids round. Them, me and Alfie, Mum and Dad. There'd been eight of us in the room.

"I've been deliberately dropping the number eight around you as much as possible since I got back from tour. Subliminal messaging. Sometimes you noticed, sometimes you didn't. So then, when the moment of truth came and you chose a number between one and ten, which one did you pick?"

And *that's* when I saw the woman in green for the final time. We'd just crested a hill and were gaining speed. She was running towards us along the adjacent pavement. But this time was different from the others. This time there was no blood. Her head was upright, her neck unbroken.

We drove towards her. She ran towards us.

And suddenly, I understood.

I slammed on the brakes. Alfie and I jerked forwards as the car decelerated. I tried to swerve away, but an oncoming van forced us to stay in our lane.

We were almost on top of her. The woman in green tripped. Her ankle twisted and she staggered and her eyes gaped with panic and her arms flailed in vain, but there was nothing to grab onto.

She fell straight into the road.

Our tyres screeched and our seat belts gouged our chests. I was screaming. Alfie was screaming. The woman disappeared under the bonnet. I leaned out the window and the suspension *clonk*ed as we skidded to a halt... with the front tyre mere inches from the woman in green's neck.

She dragged herself back onto the pavement; shaking, sweating, and staring up at the car like it was the underside of a monstrous foot.

Beside me, Alfie was hyperventilating. "You... started braking before... before she even fell." He gawked up at me, looking tiny and sounding even tinier. "How did you... know?"

I clung desperately to the steering wheel.

"A magic trick," I whispered.

Animal Wall

BY TAZ RAHMAN

*To begin at the beginning: the whimsical heron Annabelle, sometimes
shapeshifting to a songbird, sometimes, in human form, dips in and out of
tales old and new fifty steps around Cardiff Castle, where one spring, for
the first time, the wandering soul feels a sense of belonging.*

I

After the pews are cold
after morning service
after the loiterers are gone
St. John sniffs the city stalls.

Sprat and turbot at market's gate
figs and fennel in autumn mist
waft of Cornwall
Ten Feet Tall.

Evening falls on red-cheeked
Adam, Jamie, Annmarie,
they drink dry the skull of Glyndwr
clutching their little red books.

Old Owain under the cover
in a mass brawl
gawks at an oval
eighty thousand growl.

Here, I saw Gareth Edwards
hands in pocket
sniffing cinnamon
walk past the Christmas stall.

*

Pass the American king
under the barrister's chamber
into the arcade
then turn left

fifty steps north
stands the wall
where in a gale
I first met Annabelle.

That night
my brolly protested
in feeble fight, bowed
in respect, inside out.

A lost Anna, bell-grey heron
soaring above the Nile
dunking Geneva
steaming Thames

66

and a short haul after
in the dead of night
she screamed
on the banks of Taff.

Over a cuppa
astride me
I pinned to a bed -
she then flapped

of all the castles she had seen
from Bushey to Brecon
never had she seen
an animal wall.

II

Damp seeps through
the fort of Taff
where the water drips
the visitor strays

shadows run
day and night
in sentries fossilised
towers eek saints

Teilo, Illtud, Canna
to the low hills west
the castle grout
in the dark, curates rot.

North-wall brambles
the magnolia shed
swallows stir, squirrels sew
a pink-white quilt.

Magpies descend, inspect patterns
feast on succulent worms
observe as corvids do
in watchful nods.

*

Priscilla pelican
lost her eyes
eyes that once glinted
morning to coal.

On her wall mutter
the racoon, the beaver
the vulture and the wolf
the lynx shakes head

washes up seal
snorts dry anteater
a heron, daubed in grime,
stills the animal wall.

*

Life on walls:
a moat parched
in hot summer thirst
school breaks

summer swarms
upon the teenage lithe
bewitched fragrant weed
lined next to twisted dreams,

armies of St. John,
virgins for St. Mary
baffled monks at
Greyfriars, Blackfriars

grope Molly, Charlie, Mandy
the sky sings late in dark
a hymn to sobriety
in nightjar prayer.

*

By the wall
pitches bereave
the lonely man
who once was a boy

the night love-spooned
moon-beams now so quiet
pat the coat-tails
of old Captain Morgan.

III

Steps to the north
past the moat
a path held in metal strips
stones crushed

sprinkled on gravel,
to the side
is the foot-deep brook.
In tiny steps

the pupper
dips his toes
runs down water
stirs mud.

Wild mushrooms
yellow, pink
sundrenched soaks
doggo splash.

*

Off the steps
the metal strips
the old path that lace
morning trysts

daisies hold back
footsteps
the chancer
pleasure-seeker

man and dog
woman and mog
dandelions look over the side
where dance The Royal Welsh -

Bergman
Harold Arlen
Hoagy Carmichael
with them sings Annabelle

"What are you doing the rest of your life
North and South and East and West of your life
I have only one request of your life
That you spend it all with me"

her voice soaring
above the bridge
wood croaking
spinning spokes

the path of man
stare down late April
a wild garlic bloom
across the bank.

IV

Under a giant leaf
the last note sung
wakes heron
coos goodbye

in her green-eyed smile
to the mute swans
sweet glide
above the notes of long

over the arched-low-bridge
where the moat stream
hides in ventricles of moss
the castle streets

queens
the paths of Bute
gleaming Altolusso
the coot and lotus stream

there in the shade
of the hunched tree
by the canal feeding a wharf
rests Annabelle.

*

When Zephyr rides
late in Spring
the mist turns mizzle
murmurs a toad

enraptured flies cling heron
there in the canal green
springs new life
to sit upon the castle wall.

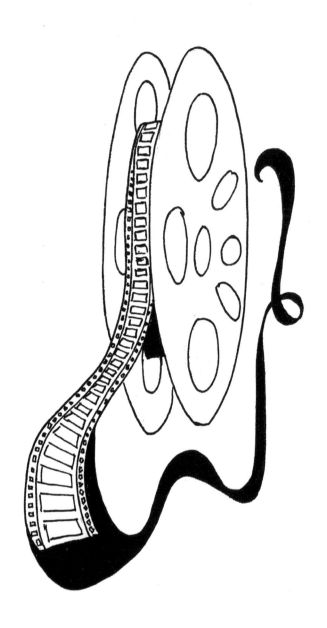

On Writing Creative Non-Fiction

PHIL OKWEDY

I'm not an actual historian. I'm an unreliable narrator. Kara Walker, *Artist*

Setting out to write creative nonfiction, I held certain assumptions and didn't really give the act of remembering a second thought. One assumption was that my memory of events would be sketchy, and to make it scan for the reader I would need to fill things in – the creative bit. Another assumption was that memory functioned like a vast film archive in the mind. I could simply go to the shelf, pull out the tape I wanted, and the memory recorded would be as pristine as the day I first experienced it. Untouched by time, save that the quality of the film might have deteriorated, leaving images blurry and the sound track choppy. This was the nonfiction bit.

But it turns out, for me at least, this is not the case at all. Rather than an archive, my memory is more like an editing suite where films are perpetually undergoing the process of selection, cutting, and splicing with new material so that meaning is constantly being updated. The discovery I made in trying to write a memoir is that memory is quantum. Just as in quantum mechanics, where measuring something changes the properties of the thing being measured, the act of remembering changes the memory itself. This means, while trawling my memories, I have had to face the fact that I am, at best, an unreliable narrator, and at worst, a compulsive liar who can never quite fix the truth of things.

Take this for example:

Remember the long, hot summer of 1976...it was something else, man!

In case you don't...we had a heatwave that lasted from late June all the way to the beginning of the August bank holiday weekend. It included 15 straight days of temperatures above 30°C; the longest such spell ever recorded in Britain.

Reservoirs emptied, their muddy bottoms cracking as they were baked solid. Across the country tarmac melted on roads and motorways. You couldn't walk down my local high street without crushing the thousands of ladybirds that carpeted the pavements. They got everywhere, in your hair, up your nose, in your food. But for me and Suzi Quatro, it wasn't the plague of seven-spotted aphid-eaters that made 1976 such a memorable year, nor the plumes of smoke that would suddenly appear on the horizon as another grassland fire raged, or even the stickers and t-shirts that advised us to "Save Water! Bathe with A Friend." No, for me and Suzi Quatro, it was that 1976 was our first summer of love.

We were 14 years old and inseparable.

Okay, that wasn't her real name, but she had the same hair and feisty attitude as Suzi Q. When one of her brothers tried to warn her off from 'going with a black boy' she was having none of it. And, after he cornered me in an alley one night, she gave me the courage not to crumble in the face of his threats.

So far, so true. Only not quite. Factually, it is as accurate as 45-year-old memory can be. The claim that Suzi Q gave me courage, is not.

It wasn't courage I felt back then but shame. Shame that I was too cowardly to stand up to her brother in that alley. Shame, as the years went by, that I had not confronted racism when I'd so blatantly encountered it. But to keep the precious memory of first love alive, each remembering consolidated the idea that it was courage that Suzi Q gave me, and this became even more important because of what happened next.

Thanks to lifts into town on the back of my brother's motorbike, Suzi and I spent evening after balmy evening that summer joshing and snogging and hanging around until darkness began to draw down and it was time to catch a lift home.

That is, until one Saturday night in August.

I was in the toilet at the local disco, when the bloke standing next to me said, "You're Phil?"

I say bloke but I'd soon learn that he was only a couple of years older than me and a boy soldier. But standing there that night, staring down at me from above his moustache, he seemed as tall and as broad as at least two of me.

He went on, "You go out with Suzi Quatro?"

I nodded.

"Not anymore. I go out with her now!"

For a moment, we just stood there looking at each other as the muffled sound of Elton John and Kiki Dee imploring each other...Don't go breaking my heart, don't go breaking my...don't go breaking my heart...filtered out of the main hall.

"All right!" he said and was gone.

Again, this did really happen, although when I now recall it there is no sound at all, no song playing, and the bloke's words are imagined because I can no longer hear them – though they do hold the truth of what he said.

More importantly though, I said nothing, I did not challenge him in any way, not verbally or physically. In the memory this has always been because I was sensitive and understood right away that she was lost to me. That fighting would not get her back. But what I really felt at the time was the same cowardly shame I'd experienced in the alley. I'd failed to stand up to him and, somewhere deep in my soul, I've never been able to completely bury the notion that a kind of latent racism lay behind the way he so nonchalantly dismissed me.

But here I go again, re-remembering, molding the past to shape current needs. My memory, that unreliable narrator, lying to me, and to you in order to preserve the precious memory of first love. Time would reveal that Suzi Q didn't choose just any bloke over me. This was the bloke she would marry, have a family with and be very happy with, until they weren't anymore.

In the end, that he was the right bloke for Suzi Q is what keeps the recollection of that long, hot summer of 1976 so special. He was the right bloke and in not standing up to him or questioning his motives, I did the right thing.

Trouble is, now you know that's not true. Memory is a liar, but the question is, what kind of liar? Compulsive or pathological? A compulsive liar lies out of habit; a pathological liar lies to get their own way. I leave it to you to decide.

How can someone draw a map without lines, and why they should want to

UMULKHAYR MOHAMED

For someone who sees themselves as a writer perhaps I am too tough on definitions, my reflexes reducing them to their limiting edges, my matter pushing back in the way it has been conditioned to, leaving little space for the valuing of the meanings that only their articulations can provide.

Well (adverb) [formal]. You'd say to clarify something you have just said. *Women are the drawers of short straws. Well, at least in relation to Gender Politics.*

Women (countable noun) [informal]. People sometimes refer to someone's wife, or girlfriend as their women. *Their women are so self-confident, they must draw it from their sense of belonging.*

Welsh (adjective) [formal]. Welsh means belonging or relation to Wales, or to its people, language, or culture.

Are we right to see it this way, would it be less correct to view Wales as belonging to the Welsh? What would be the logical conclusion of this mirrored definition be?

Do you see the problem I am faced with when it comes to maps and mapping?

Where is the appreciation for Context – "How can we define ourselves, without calling on the definition of others?" This process and its necessity needs to be represented also.

What about Conjuncture – 'A state of affairs', is that not another kind of nature, one that mapping would be useful for?

Lines feel so underwhelming here, in their inability to reveal what lies under them. Why not draw zones instead shaped like wells? Each holding their value under the surface, but allowing for the possibility of overflowing into one another, when nature calls them to. And what if this was the case, would we have the capacity to read this not as an overburdening, but a sharing instead?

See borders bleed more the closer you get to them. Have you ever visited a city split across a border? My grandmother has many times enroute to Ethiopia, she says this city functions the same way any other city does, but of course why wouldn't it when it's not really split at all.

> *Ask me when I'll know it's ready,*
> *Know I must be mapping.*
>
> *Ask me what we can fill it with,*
> *Know I must be mapping.*

They have done studies on this, Women tend to give directions using visible landmarks, Men by distance and direction. They, the scientists who did these studies, do not speak of how other genders / non-genders approach this task so I cannot relay this to you, this is the kind of leaving space I do not appreciate, an absence despite the pretence of completion.

But what happens when I draw a line at each one of my wrists and gender my hands differently to the rest of me, does this mean my hands would prefer to give directions in another way? I haven't ever got my bearings and can't translate time into length, so I think they would be at a loss for words.

I ask how this can be, I turn back to maps, they reveal their transient truth as I realise, I'm surrounded by outdated editions. I cannot find my favourite tree, but I know it's on my left as I step out. I only realised I loved it five years ago. That's fifteen years of not noticing, maybe I would have realised sooner, had more love in my life if it had been laid out for me, mapped. If abstraction is a revelation through removal, perhaps it's wrong of me to ask.

I come across the nation state, that's only seeking to be in conversation with itself and nothing else, how can this be anything more than a vexed situation of seeking singularity – a seeking of wholeness, oneness in a place that cannot value it, and has not even the capacity to hold it in the way the ephemeral was built to.

Hear me, can you hear me now,
amongst the shuffling of the crowd a
shift to the right, a breeze in the air
their drawing lines without a care.

And in the tradition of leaving space, as I have sought to lay out here, I must also leave space for the brutal possibility that all I truly seek is a style of seeing the world that has not yet been defined, its freedom flirting and destined to die as soon as its essence is captured, and in my earnestness to tie it down and look a little closer I have killed it already.

Maps and Rooms

Biographies

Shara Atashi is an author and translator based in Aberystwyth. Her work has been published at *Writers Mosaic, New Welsh Review* and *Modern Poetry in Translation*. She was awarded a place by Literature Wales to develop and represent their campaign for writers of colour. A section of her book From *The Claws Of A Long Verse* will be featured in *New Welsh Reader*'s summer edition.

Emily Burnett is a writer and BAFTA-winning actress. She has written for BBC Radio with one-off drama *H is for Hair*, and is a part of the BBC Writer's Room Welsh Voices cohort of 2019/20. Her writing often centres around the visibility of unrepresented voices and communities, looking at how we can amplify unheard voices. She is working on two original television ideas.

Daniel Howell is 22 and from Carmarthen. Having always loved reading, Daniel knew by the time he was a teenager that writing a novel himself was inevitable. He is currently working on a number of projects, including a horror novella and a series of 12 science fiction novellas.

Jaffrin is a Welsh Bangladeshi writer and visual artist based in Cardiff and London. Citing Def Poetry Jam poets as a form of inspiration for her spoken word, religion and identity are key motivations in the body of her work. She had started writing and performing poetry as a form of activism, to work through personal traumas and discuss topics that are deemed taboo in South Asian communities such as relationships, body image, feminism, injustice and religion.

Umulkhayr Mohamed is a Welsh Somali writer and artist, who also produces work under the alias, Aisha Ajnabi, their art other. Her artistic practice involves primarily poetry, artist moving image, installation and performance work that explores the tension present between enjoying the act of wandering between emancipatory temporalities and a functional need to position oneself in the now. Their art is the place where they are able to forgo pretences and hierarchies, replacing them with solidarity and liberation, a way for them to contribute to doing the work of eroding the borders between beings to reveal the wholeness that lays beneath.

Biographies

Nia Morais is a writer and playwright from Cardiff. She is interested in short story, audio drama, fantasy and horror genres. Nia is a Welsh-Cape Verdean writer who recently graduated with a Master's in Creative Writing from Cardiff University. Their work usually focuses on themes of identity and survival.

Phil Okwedy is 58 and from Pembrokeshire. Born in Cardiff of a Welsh mother and Nigerian father, he is an oral performance storyteller and myth-maker who draws deeply on his dual heritage and multiple cultures in order to find the contemporary in the traditional. He regularly performs in storytelling clubs and has featured at Beyond the Border and Aberystwyth Storytelling Festivals, as well as at Kea Festival in Greece and Fabula Festival in Sweden. His first book, *Wil & the Welsh Black Cattle*, is a set of Welsh folktales framed around the mythology of the ancient cattle drovers.

Taz Rahman is a Cardiff based writer of Bengali origin. He has been published or is forthcoming in *Poetry Wales, Bad Lilies, South Bank Poetry, Anthropocene, Honest Ulsterman, Nation Cymru, Culture Matters* and in various anthologies. He is in the editorial team for the climate change themed new literary magazine *Modron*. He judged the 2021 Poetry Wales Pamphlet Competition and is a peer reviewer for the Books Council Wales. He is the founder of the Youtube poetry channel 'Just Another Poet.'

Durre Shahwar is a writer, editor, and a Future Wales Fellowship artist (collaboration between Arts Council Wales and Natural Resources Wales). She is the co-founder of 'Where I'm Coming From' open mic collective. Durre is currently doing a PhD in Creative Writing at Cardiff University while writing her debut book.

Marvin Thompson was born in London to Jamaican parents and now lives in south Wales. In 2021, he made headlines by winning the Poetry Society's National Poetry Competition. He was the first poet of colour to win since 1981. His debut poetry collection, *Road Trip*, is a Poetry Book Society Recommendation and shortlisted for the Wales Book of the Year Award, 2021. In December 2021, Thompson stepped down from the Representing Wales cohort to pursue a new and exciting career with Literature Wales.